This
Treasure Cove Story
belongs to

_____

I AM A PRINCESS

A CENTUM BOOK 978-1-912396-68-9
Published in Great Britain by Centum Books Ltd.
This edition published 2018.

3 5 7 9 10 8 6 4 2

Centum Books Ltd, 20 Devon Square, Newton Abbot,
Devon, TQ12 2HR, UK.

www.centumbooksltd.co.uk | books@centumbooksltd.co.uk
CENTUM BOOKS Limited Reg.No. 07641486.

A CIP catalogue record for this book is available
from the British Library.

Printed in China.

centum

DISNEY
PRINCESS

I Am a Princess

By Andrea Posner-Sanchez

Illustrated by

Francesco Legramandi

and Gabriella Matta

Hello! My name is Cinderella. I am a princess. I live in a beautiful castle and have lots of fancy gowns and jewels. But not all princesses are the same – we each enjoy doing our own special thing.

I love caring for animals...

...and having them care for me!

I am Ariel.

I love to sing. Sometimes my sisters and
I perform concerts for our father, King Triton.

I also love to collect treasures from the human world. This statue of Prince Eric is my favourite!

Hello! I am Snow White.

I like to have fun with my friends Happy, Sleepy, Sneezy, Grumpy, Doc, Bashful and Dopey...

...and then surprise them with a sweet treat.

My name is Tiana and I love to cook!

Even when I was a frog, I made a tasty gumbo for my friends – Prince Naveen, Louis and Ray.

Now I get to make lots of people happy
with my food – at my very own restaurant!

Hello! I am Rapunzel.

I love to paint pictures...

...and play with Pascal.
He is really good at hide and seek!

My name is Aurora.

When I was a baby, I was given
the gift of song, so I love music.

Now I enjoy dancing with Prince Phillip
whenever we get the chance!

Hello! I am Jasmine.

I love going on adventures with Aladdin beside me!

Bonjour! I am Belle.

I love to read all kinds of books.

I even like to read about other princesses. Don't you?

Treasure Cove Stories

Book list may be subject to change.